Kama Sutra

India Book Distributors (Bombay) Ltd.

Publisher : **MELROY DICKSON**
Photographer : **RUPINDER KHULLAR**
Text : **ASHARANI MATHUR**

Published by India Book Distributors
(Bombay) Ltd.,
1007/1008 Arcadia, 195 Nariman Point,
Bombay 400 021
Tel. : 22 46 46/22 46 91/287 25 28/
287 25 32.
Telex : 011-86085 IBD IN
Fax : 022-287 25 31
Copyright © IBD 1994
Copyright © Photographs Rupinder Khullar
Copyright © Text AshaRani Mathur

ISBN 81-7310-047-0

Printed at Thomson Press (India) Ltd.

Kama Sutra

RUPINDER KHULLAR
ASHARANI MATHUR

THE KAMA SUTRA, a historical and literary classic which is at least 2000 years old, is not only one of the greatest works of Hindu thought, it is also the most misunderstood. Because of its connotations of eroticism and the techniques of love-making, it has been variously considered as a "how to" sex manual, or, worse still, as a work of classical pornography, beautiful but nonetheless salacious.

Nothing could be further from the truth. Of its seven chapters, or groups of aphorisms, only one deals in detail with the explication of the various types of sexual union. The other six are remarkable descriptions of the context of love, and of the entire relationship between man and woman, at the heart of which lies that coming together which is not just physical but emotional and even spiritual. Because people are part of a community, the Kama Sutra elaborates with some minuteness on social observances. Today, centuries after it was first compiled, it remains a document of great contemporary relevance, for societies may have undergone mutations, but basic human needs have not. The most surprising element of the Kama Sutra, then, is not necessarily the sexual athleticism it sometimes describes, but the fact that our hunger for tenderness and communication remains as real today as it did a millennium ago. And the fact that the means for satisfying that hunger are precisely those described by Vatsyayana.

The Kama Sutra as expounded by Mallinaga Vatsyayana (to give him his full name) is itself a distillation of the love teachings of previous texts, those of Nandi, Svetaketu and Babhravya. Babhravya's 150 chapters grouped under seven heads had commentaries by different learned men. From this vast accumulation of wisdom, Vatsyayana drew out his own slender volume as an abstract, a summary, of all that had been propounded before. And he structured it in the form of *sutras*, aphorisms or precepts, tempered as much by humanism as by rationalism and moral uprightness.

To begin with, Vatsyayana places Kama (variously and loosely interpreted as desire, affection, love, lust, sensual pleasure) within its context as one of the three principle goals of human life, the other two being Dharma and Artha. These three goals, known as the *trivarga*, or three-fold aims, are to be attempted in this life, according to ancient Hindu thought. All three are fairly complex concepts, but to express them simply — Dharma is the path of right action in accordance with the Holy Writ, of righteousness, of ethical principles. Artha is the pursuit of economic interests, the accumulation of wealth and material goods. Kama is the conscious enjoyment of sensual pleasures. Man must practise all three; each at the appropriate time and in such a manner that they may harmonize. Though Dharma is recognised as being superior to Artha, and that in turn to Kama, Vatsyayana enjoins the practice of all three for happiness, a nice balance between spiritual, material and sensual objectives.

But the practice of Dharma and Artha requires study, skill, application, whereas that of Kama is to be found everywhere and done even by brute creatures. It does not need to be taught, so why then the Kama Sutra? Not so, says Vatsyayana, sexual pleasures are as basic to the human being as is food and drink. The knowledge of the nuances of these pleasures simply enhances them. Kama is the natural outcome of Dharma and Artha; it is one of the joys of human existence, and to be well-versed in its arts is necessary. After all, if married love is part of Dharma, there is merit in doing one's duty well.

Thus the famous definition of Kama as "the enjoyment of appropriate objects by the five senses of hearing, feeling, seeing, tasting and smelling, assisted by the mind together with the soul. The ingredient in this is a peculiar contact between the organ of sense and its object, and the consciousness of pleasure which arises from that contact is called Kama". The personification is the god Kama, the god of Love, who is young and carries a bow of sugarcane strung with humming bees with five lotus flower tipped arrows.

Having laid the framework for his precepts, Vatsyayana proceeds to specifics. In Part I, he recommends that young maidens should study the 64 love techniques enumerated by Babhravya, and they should also know the 64 arts and sciences, including singing, dancing, painting, flower decoration, swimming and water games, cooking, sewing, improvising poetry, dice and chess, chemistry, carpentry, cock fighting, gymnastics.

Part II (of which more later) is about sexual union. Part III is about acquiring a wife, on courtship, betrothal, marriage and its forms, and on winning the confidence of the young bride. Part IV is about the wife and her duties, which include keeping her home clean and her person attractive, perfumed and jewelled for her husband, running a kitchen garden, laying out gardens with flowers, trees and a lotus pond, practising budgetary restraints and economies, and not being a nag or a shrew. Vatsyayana also describes her ideal behaviour with others, in-laws, co-wives, in a harem. Part V is on other men's wives and extra-marital affairs, an interesting reflection of prevalent social mores which has a ring of truth even today. Part VI is about courtesans, their co-habiting with men, their obtaining money from their lovers, their gains and losses, and how to get rid of a lover. Part VII is about aphrodisiacs, love potions, and unguents used for making oneself attractive, enslaving a lover or enlarging the male organ.

This sketchy and bare-bones outline of the Kama Sutra admittedly does the text little justice. It does, however, give some idea of the context in which Vatsyayana placed the sexual act. For he viewed it as not merely a physical act to satisfy an urgent need; its consummation required leisure and a delicacy of approach which resulted in the willing participation of both man and woman. The scene for seduction (by either side) was set as much by light airy rooms and soft, flower-strewn beds with silken canopies, as by charm, sparkling conversation and the offering of wines and *paan* (betel leaf). To use force is not recommended, for it is a brute act leading to fear and repulsion. Nor is physical pleasure the sole end of love-making, just as love-making comprises an entire set of activities and not only the sexual act. How to teach men and women to accept each other's feelings, and to respond to each other overcoming fear, shyness and inexperience, is a basic premise of the Kama Sutra. And Vatsyayana, accepting the uniqueness of each couple and their circumstances, goes on to say that there can be no rigid rules in the matter of love, only experience teaches mutual satisfaction.

The most famous part of the Kama Sutra is, of course, the second, which deals with sexual union. Here Vatsyayana dwells on a fundamental point — compatibility between man and woman. This compatibility is measured through the size of the organs, the force of passion or carnal desire, and the length of time of performance. In his now famous description, Vatsyayana speaks of man as hare, bull or horse, and woman as deer, mare or elephant, depending on the size of their organs. The best match is between the hare man and the deer woman, the bull man and mare woman and the horse man and the elephant woman. Six other combinations are, however, possible, with greater or lesser degrees of mismatch. Similarly, nine combinations each are possible in the areas of force of passion and length of timing. Vatsyayana seems to suggest that though dimensions and temperament may cause mismatches, some degree of compensation is possible through the skilled practice of the right technique.

The apocryphal 64 is now dealt with, the celebrated techniques of love making so-called supposedly because eight techniques are elaborated under each of eight headings — embraces, kisses, nailmarks, love-bites, the postures of congress, love cries, role reversal and oral sex. This is not strictly true and 64 is probably used in a symbolic rather than literal manner. As Vatsyayana takes us through this catalogue of sexual possibilities (with, I suspect, some impossibilities!) his descriptions are sometimes clinical and sometimes poetic. The very names "the climbing of a creeper" or "the climbing of a tree" seem to evoke the embraces they describe. Kissing, that essential prelude, is not only of various kinds, but can be used playfully in a delightful game of love. The intensely passionate lover marks the body of the beloved by pressing or scratching with the fingernails, or through love bites with the teeth ("the line of jewels", "the broken cloud"). All these are seen as part of foreplay, though not exclusively, "for love does not care for time or order".

After this are described the various positions of sexual

congress (some of which are almost gymnastic in nature) and the variations of oral sex. In the concluding part, Vatsyayana paints us a pretty picture of post-coital lovers. Bathed, their bruises salved by perfumed ointments, refreshed by partaking of fruit juices and light snacks, they sit clasped together in an open air terrace watching the moonlight. "A man skilled in the sixty four parts is looked upon with love by his own wife, the wives of others and courtesans."

Many of the sexual positions described in the Kama Sutra have been depicted in Indian art, most notably in temple sculpture and in painting. The most famous sculptures are those at Konarak and Khajuraho, voluptuous yet sublime. Much smaller, and therefore on a more human scale, are the paintings. These were commissioned by rich patrons as folios for private viewing, or to share with a partner to stimulate desire. Whatever the raison-d'etre of these art forms, they are unabashedly explicit; equally, they are free of guilt and shame, making a physical act into the intimate union of equals. For, says Vatsyayana, all desire springs from nature; when such desire is polished by technique and touched by wisdom, it becomes firm and secure. To partake of pleasure for the deepest mutual satisfaction is both an art and a science that must be learned, for "he who knows how to make himself beloved by women, as well as to increase their honour and create confidence in them, becomes an object of their love."

"Even young maids should study this Kama Sutra,
along with its arts and sciences, before marriage."

"Together with the
Kama Sutra, the arts to
be studied include
colouring ... the hair,
nails and bodies."

"The art of dressing the hair with unguents and perfumes ..."

"Proper disposition of jewels and decorations ..."

"Art of applying perfumed ointments to the body ..."

"Even the daughters of
Kings, being learned in
the above arts, can
make their husbands
favourable to them,
though these may have
thousands of other
wives ..."

"Kama is the enjoyment of appropriate objects by the five senses, assisted by the mind together with the soul."

"The contact between the organ of sense and its object, and the consciousness of pleasure from that contact, is called Kama."

(Upper) "On the occasion of first congress, kissing should be done moderately."

(Lower) "When the lips of two lovers are brought into direct contact with each other, it is called a 'straight kiss'."

"Even those embraces that are not mentioned in the Kama Sutra should be practiced at the time of sexual enjoyment, if they are conducive to the increase of love or passion."

"When lovers lie on a bed and embrace so closely that the arms and thighs of one are encircled by the arms and thighs of the other, this is called the mixture of sesame seed with rice."

"When a woman, clinging to a man as a creeper twines round a tree, bends his head down to hers, it is called an embrace like the twining of a creeper."

"When a man enjoys many women altogether, it is called the 'congress of a herd of cows'."

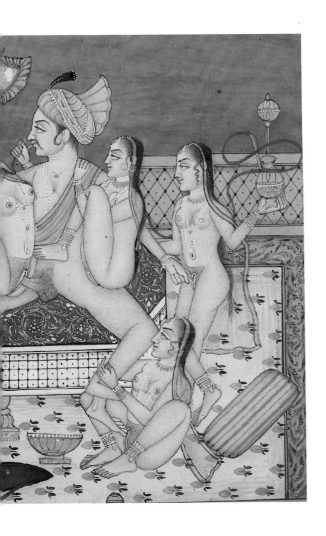

"When a man and a woman
support themselves on each
other's bodies, or on a wall or
pillar, and while standing
engage in congress, it is called
the 'supported congress'."

"When the Deer Woman raises her thighs and keeps them wide apart, it is called the 'yawning position'."

"When the woman places one of her legs on her lover's shoulder and stretches the other out, and continues to do so alternately, it is called the 'splitting of a bamboo'."

"When a woman stands on her hands and feet like a quadruped and her lover mounts her like a bull, it is called the 'congress of a cow'."

"An ingenious person should multiply the kinds of congress after the fashion of the different kinds of beasts and of birds."

33

"The congress that takes place between two
persons who are attached to one another, and
which is done according to their liking, is called
'spontaneous congress '. "

"Love which is mutual and proved to be true, when each looks upon the other as his or her very own, that is called love resulting from belief."

Auparishtaka, the oral congress.

"The 'nominal congress', holding the man's lingam with the
hand and placing it between the lips."

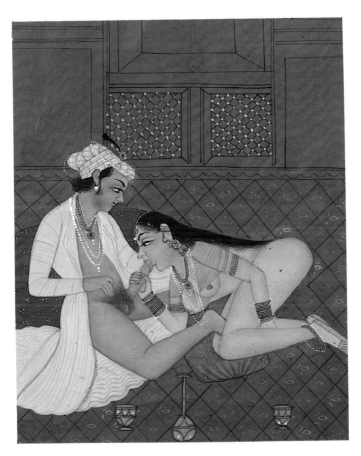

"When after kissing the lingam, it is touched with the tongue everywhere, it is called 'rubbing'."

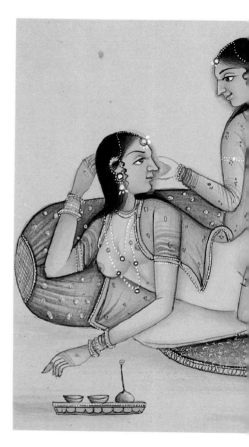

"Some Kings, who are compassionate, apply certain medicines to enable them to enjoy many wives in one night, simply for the purpose of satisfying the desire of their women."

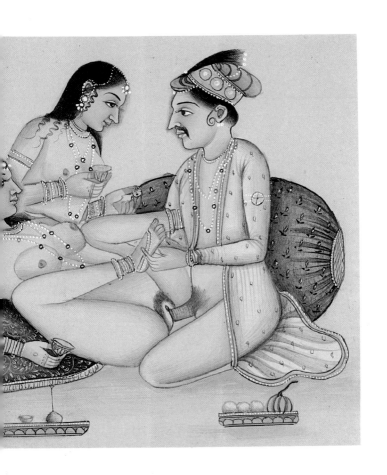

"A loving pair become blind with passion in the
heat of congress, and go on with great impetuosity,
paying not the least regard to excess."

"When a man enjoys two women together,
both of whom love him equally, it is
called the 'united congress'."

45

"The whole subject of embracing is such that men who ask questions about it, or who hear or talk about it, acquire a desire for enjoyment."

"The lovers may also sit on the terrace of the palace or house, and enjoy the moonlight."

47

"When a woman sees that her lover is fatigued by constant congress, she should give him assistance by acting his part."

"When, on such an occasion, the man lifts up
the middle part of his body, and the woman
turns round her middle part, it is called the
'swing'."

"Desire, which springs from nature, and which is
increased by art, and from which all danger is taken
away by wisdom, becomes firm and secure."

"Men who generally obtain success with women are those well versed in the science of love and who are celebrated for being very strong."

"As variety is necessary in love, so love is to be produced by means of variety."

"If variety is sought in all the arts and amusements, how much more should it be sought after in the art of love."

"When a man and a woman lie down in an inverted order, with the head of one toward the feet of the other, and carry on this (oral) congress, it is called the 'congress of a crow'."

"Though a woman is reserved and keeps her feelings concealed, yet when she gets on top of a man, she shows all her love and desire."

"Blows should be given on the back of a woman while she is sitting on the lap of the man, and she should give blows in return."

"When either of the lovers touches the forehead of the other with his or her own, it is called the 'embrace of the forehead'."

"There is a difference in the consciousness of pleasure, for a man thinks, 'This woman is united with me' and a woman thinks, 'I am united with this man'."

"When the wheel of love is once set in motion,
there is then no Shastra and no order."

"When she lowers her head and raises her
middle parts, it is called the 'widely opened
position'."

"An ointment made of the fruit of the **kokilaksha,** *will contract the yoni of a Hastini, or elephant woman."*

"He who knows how to make himself beloved by
women, as well as to increase their honour,
becomes an object of their love."

"He should gain over
a girl that loves him,
by having recourse to
persons in whom she
confides."

"A man marrying many wives should act fairly toward them all ... he should please them all by loving unions."

"Men and women being of
the same nature feel the same
kind of pleasure, and
therefore a man should marry
such a woman as will love
him ever afterward."